Take a Closer Look

Authors, Consultants, and Reviewers

MULTICULTURAL AND EDUCATIONAL
CONSULTANTS

Alma Flor Ada, Yvonne Beamer, Joyce Buckner,
Helen Gillotte, Cheryl Hudson, Narcita Medina,
Lorraine Monroe, James R. Murphy, Sylvia Peña,
Joseph B. Rubin, Ramon Santiago, Cliff Trafzer,
Hai Tran, Esther Lee Yao

LITERATURE CONSULTANTS

Ashley Bryan, Joan I. Glazer, Paul Janeczko,
Margaret H. Lippert

INTERNATIONAL CONSULTANTS

Edward B. Adams, Barbara Johnson,
Raymond L. Marshall

MUSIC AND AUDIO CONSULTANTS

John Farrell, Marilyn C. Davidson,
Vincent Lawrence, Sarah Pirtle, Susan R. Synder,
Rick and Deborah Witkowski, Eastern Sky Media
Services, Inc.

TEACHER REVIEWERS

Terry Baker, Jane Bauer, James Bedi, Nora Bickel,
Vernell Bowen, Donald Cason, Jean Chaney,
Carolyn Clark, Alan Cox, Kathryn DesCarpentrie,
Carol L. Ellis, Roberta Gale, Brenda Huffman,
Erma Inscore, Sharon Kidwell, Elizabeth Love,
Isabel Marcus, Elaine McCraney, Michelle Moraros,
Earlene Parr, Dr. Richard Potts, Jeanette Pulliam,
Michael Rubin, Henrietta Sakamaki,
Kathleen Cultron Sanders, Belinda Snow,
Dr. Jayne Steubing, Margaret Mary Sulentic,
Barbara Tate, Seretta Vincent,
Willard Waite, Barbara Wilson, Veronica York

Macmillan/McGraw-Hill

A Division of The **McGraw-Hill** Companies

Macmillan/McGraw-Hill
1221 Avenue of the Americas
New York, New York 10020

Printed in the United States of America

ISBN 0-02-181113-X / 1, L.4, U.1
2 3 4 5 6 7 8 9 R R W 02 01 00 99 98 97

Take a Closer Look

AUTHORS

ELAINE MEI AOKI • VIRGINIA ARNOLD • JAMES FLOOD • JAMES V. HOFFMAN • DIANE LAPP

MIRIAM MARTINEZ • ANNEMARIE SULLIVAN PALINCSAR • MICHAEL PRIESTLEY • CARL B. SMITH

WILLIAM H. TEALE • JOSEFINA VILLAMIL TINAJERO • ARNOLD W. WEBB • KAREN D. WOOD

McGraw Hill Macmillan McGraw-Hill

NEW YORK • FARMINGTON

Contents

Hattie
and the
Fox

Written by Mem Fox
Illustrated by Patricia Mullins

Hattie was a big black hen.
One morning she looked up and said,
"Goodness gracious me!
I can see a nose in the bushes!"

"Good grief!" said the goose.
"Well, well!" said the pig.

"Who cares?" said the sheep.
"So what?" said the horse.
"What next?" said the cow.

And Hattie said,
"Goodness gracious me!
I can see a nose
and two eyes in the bushes!"

"Good grief!" said the goose.
"Well, well!" said the pig.
"Who cares?" said the sheep.
"So what?" said the horse.
"What next?" said the cow.

And Hattie said,
"Goodness gracious me!
I can see a nose, two eyes,
and two ears in the bushes!"

"Good grief!" said the goose.
"Well, well!" said the pig.
"Who cares?" said the sheep.
"So what?" said the horse.
"What next?" said the cow.

And Hattie said,
"Goodness gracious me!
I can see a nose, two eyes, two ears,
and two legs in the bushes!"

"Good grief!" said the goose.
"Well, well!" said the pig.
"Who cares?" said the sheep.
"So what?" said the horse.
"What next?" said the cow.

29

And Hattie said,
"Goodness gracious me!
I can see a nose, two eyes, two ears, two legs,
and a body in the bushes!"

"Good grief!" said the goose.
"Well, well!" said the pig.
"Who cares?" said the sheep.
"So what?" said the horse.
"What next?" said the cow.

And Hattie said,
"Goodness gracious me!
I can see a nose, two eyes, two ears, a body, four legs,
and a tail in the bushes!
It's a fox! It's a fox!"
And she flew very quickly into a nearby tree.

"Oh, no!" said the goose.
"Dear me!" said the pig.
"Oh, dear!" said the sheep.
"Oh, help!" said the horse.

But the cow said, "MOO!"

so loudly that the fox was frightened and ran away.

And they were all so surprised
that none of them said anything
for a very long time.

Meet Mem Fox

When Mem Fox visits schools, she often invites children to read *Hattie and the Fox* aloud with her. She says it's lots of fun to say the words fast and then to say what the cow says in a very slow, deep voice.

Ms. Fox likes this story for other reasons, too. "There are many old stories about hens and foxes," she says. "But this one is new."

Mem Fox loves to read and write. She says, "Reading is the best way to learn how to write. Reading written words and hearing written words have taught me to write well."

Meet Patricia Mullins

To make the pictures for *Hattie and the Fox,* Patricia Mullins visited a special farm in the middle of a city. She went there every day to look at the animals and make drawings of them. "I always start my pictures by drawing live animals," she says. "I watch how they move. That helps me make them look more real in my pictures."

Later, Ms. Mullins tore pieces of colored tissue paper to look like the animals. Then she glued them down. Last, she used a crayon to draw a few lines. This way of making pictures is called collage.

OPEN

I open my eyes.

I open the curtains.

I open my mouth to say "good morning."

At breakfast time

I open the refrigerator.

"I'm going out" I say,

and open the door.

Like opening a new book,

one day starts.

Chikaoka Saori, fourth grade

ANY KIND OF DOG

by Lynn Reiser

Richard wanted a dog, any kind of dog.

But his mother said
a dog was
too much trouble,

so she gave him a caterpillar.

The caterpillar was very nice.
It looked a little like a dog,

Lhasa Apso

but it was not a dog.
Richard wanted a dog.
His mother said
a dog was too much trouble,

so she gave him a mouse.

The mouse was very nice.
It looked a little like a dog,

Chihuahua

but it was not a dog.
Richard wanted a dog.
His mother said
a dog was too much trouble,

so she gave him a baby alligator.

The baby alligator was very nice.
It looked a little like a dog,

Dachshund

but it was not a dog.
Richard wanted a dog.
His mother said
a dog was too much trouble,

so she gave him a lamb.

The lamb was very nice.
It looked a little like a dog,

Bedlington Terrier

but it was not a dog.
Richard wanted a dog.
His mother said
a dog was too much trouble,

so she gave him a pony.

The pony was very nice.
It looked a little like a dog,

Great Dane

but it was not a dog.
Richard wanted a dog.
His mother said
a dog was too much trouble,

so she gave him a lion.

The lion was very nice.
It looked a little like a dog,

Chow Chow

but it was not a dog.
Richard wanted a dog.
His mother said
a dog was too much trouble,

so she gave him a bear.

The bear was very nice.
It looked a little like a dog,

Newfoundland

but it was not a dog.

All of the animals were very nice,

but Richard still wanted a dog.

So his mother gave him a dog.

The dog was very nice.
It looked exactly like a dog.

Just a Dog

The dog was a lot of trouble,

but
it was
worth it.

Meet LYNN REISER

Lynn Reiser is a doctor. She has always loved to read and draw. A few years ago, someone asked her to draw the pictures for a book of songs. She had a great time doing them! Now she writes and draws her own books. Ms. Reiser wrote *Any Kind of Dog* when her family wanted to get a dog. She says, "I like writing because it can be shared with other people. I want children to enjoy reading as much as I do."

A "Wild" Alphabet

Do you see the alphabet letters in these pictures? They are really markings on the wings of butterflies.

This butterfly has letters on its wings too. Which ones do you see?

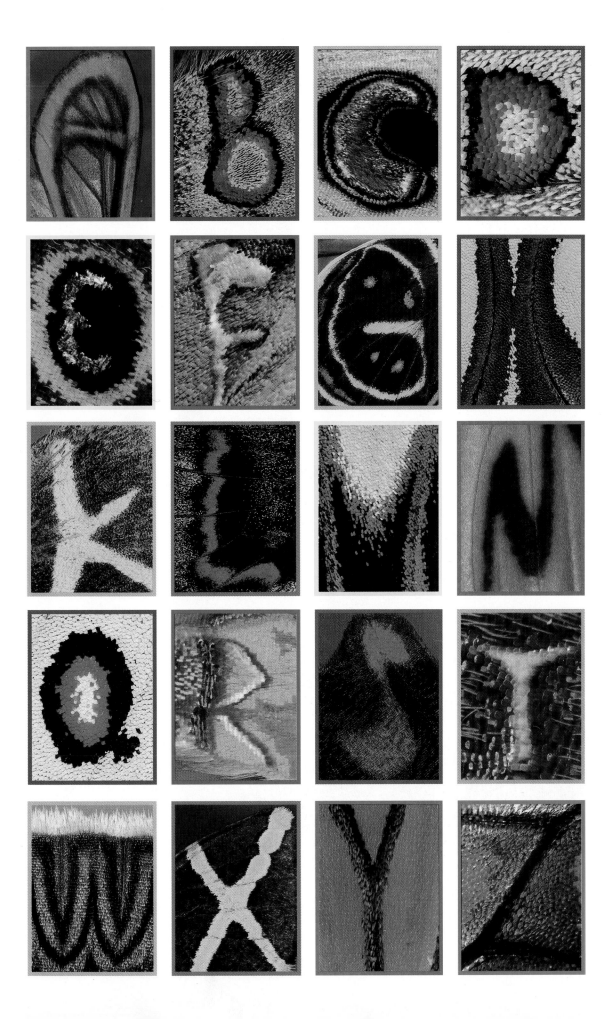

La NUBE

Nube-conejo,

nube-alacrăn,

nube-velero,

nube-volcăn,

nube-tinaja,

nube-cabeza,

nube-elefante,

nube-caleza.

Si un solo instante

miro a otro lado,

cuando me vuelvo

tŭ ya has cambiado.

Emma Pérez

The CLOUD

Cloud-rabbit,

cloud-scorpion,

cloud-sailboat,

cloud-volcano,

cloud-pitcher,

cloud-head,

cloud-elephant,

cloud-carriage.

If for a moment

I glance away,

and then turn back,

you've changed again.

Emma Pérez

Seven Sillies

Written by Joyce Dunbar

Illustrated by Chris Downing

On a bright and shining morning,
Pig looked into the pond.

"There's a pig in the pond," said Pig.
"Such a handsome pig!"

And Pig called over to Sheep.

"What do you see in the pond?" asked Pig.
"I see a pig and a sheep," answered Sheep.
"Such a beautiful sheep!"

And Sheep called over to Goat.

"What do you see in the pond?" asked Sheep.
"I see a pig and a sheep and a goat,"
answered Goat.
"Such a gorgeous goat."

And Goat called over to Rabbit.

"What do you see in the pond?" asked Goat.
"I see a pig and a sheep and a goat
and a rabbit," answered Rabbit.
"Such a splendid rabbit!"

And Rabbit called over to Hen.

"What do you see in the pond?"
asked Rabbit.
"I see a pig and a sheep and a goat and
a rabbit and a hen," said Hen.
"Such a fine, feathered hen."

And Hen called over to Mouse.

"What do you see in the pond?" asked Hen.
"I see a pig and a sheep and a goat and a
rabbit and a hen and a mouse," said Mouse.
"Such a dear, little mouse."

And Mouse called over to Frog.

"What do you see in the pond?"
asked Mouse.
"I see seven sillies," answered Frog.

"Seven sillies?" asked the pig and the sheep and the goat and the rabbit and the hen and the mouse. "What do you mean?"

"They are all in the pond and they want to get out," said Frog.
"How can we get them out?"

"You will have to jump in and fetch them," answered Frog.

So the pig and the sheep and the goat and the rabbit and the hen and the mouse all jumped into the water with a *splash!*

"There is nothing in the pond, after all!"
they said.

"Oh, yes, there is," laughed Frog.
"There is a handsome pig,
a beautiful sheep,
a gorgeous goat,

a splendid rabbit,
a fine, feathered hen,
a dear, little mouse,
and that makes seven sillies."

The animals scrambled out of the pond all
sopping and dripping with water. They did
feel very silly!

Then . . .

"How many sillies?" asked Pig.

"Seven," said Frog.

Pig began to count.

The other animals joined in.

"One, two, three, four, five, six—"
The only one left was Frog.
"Aha!" they laughed. "SEVEN SILLIES!"

"We see a frog that can't count," they said.

"Such a silly frog!"

MEET
Joyce Dunbar

Joyce Dunbar was an English teacher for many years. Then she became deaf and stopped teaching. Ms. Dunbar has always liked to write. Now she has more time to work on her writing. Her family gave her the idea to write for children. She says, "I like to write in the mornings. Then I like to spend the afternoons gardening." Even when she is not writing, she thinks about it all the time. Ms. Dunbar says she even thinks about writing in her sleep!

MEET Chris Downing

Chris Downing loves to draw and paint animals. He was happy when Joyce Dunbar asked him to illustrate *Seven Sillies*. "I am very proud of *Seven Sillies*. I hope that all children will enjoy it," he says. Chris Downing used photographs so his animals would seem real.

Mr. Downing lives in England with his wife and two small children. Sometimes he uses his family as models for his art. Chris Downing hopes to illustrate many more children's books.

First Snow

Snow makes whiteness where it falls.
The bushes look like popcorn-balls.
And places where I always play,
Look like somewhere else today.

Marie Louise Allen

Meet JAN ORMEROD

Jan Ormerod was a child in Australia when she first heard *The Story of Chicken Licken*. "In some other countries, Chicken Licken is called Chicken Little," she says.

She thought it would be fun to have this book tell two stories. "The words tell about Chicken Licken," she says. "The pictures tell another story."

At the time Ms. Ormerod wrote this story, she had a baby that crawled everywhere. "I know the trouble a crawling baby can get into," she says.

Since Ms. Ormerod wrote this book, many school-children have invited her to see their own plays and puppet shows using the Chicken Licken story.

by
Jan
Ormerod

THE STORY OF
CHICKEN
LICKEN

One day Chicken Licken
went to the woods
and an acorn fell
on her poor little head.

OH, DUCK LUCK, DON'T GO!
I was going and I met Henny Penny,
and Henny Penny met Chicken Licken
and the sky had fallen
on her poor little head.
Now we are going to tell the king.

OH, DRAKE LAKE, DON'T GO!
I was going and I met Cock Lock,
and Cock Lock met Henny Penny,
and Henny Penny met Chicken Licken
and the sky had fallen
on her poor little head.
Now we are going to tell the king.

OH, GOOSE LOOSE, DON'T GO!
I was going and I met Duck Luck,
and Duck Luck met Cock Lock,
and Cock Lock met Henny Penny,
and Henny Penny met Chicken Licken
and the sky had fallen
on her poor little head.
Now we are going to tell the king.

OH, GANDER LANDER, DON'T GO!
I was going and I met Drake Lake,
and Drake Lake met Duck Luck,
and Duck Luck met Cock Lock,
and Cock Lock met Henny Penny,
and Henny Penny met Chicken Licken
and the sky had fallen
on her poor little head.
Now we are going to tell the king.

OH, TURKEY LURKEY, DON'T GO!
I was going and I met Goose Loose,
and Goose Loose met Drake Lake,
and Drake Lake met Duck Luck,
and Duck Luck met Cock Lock,
and Cock Lock met Henny Penny,
and Henny Penny met
Chicken Licken and the sky
had fallen on her poor little head.
Now we are going to tell the king.

Foxy Woxy took them
into the fox's hole.
He and his young ones
soon ate up poor Chicken Licken,
Henny Penny, Cock Lock, Duck Luck,
Drake Lake, Goose Loose,
Gander Lander and Turkey Lurkey.
So they never saw the king
and they never told him
that the sky had fallen.

Magic in Mother

A Story Without Words by Sally Lucas

Gooseland

Illustrated by Liisa Chauncy Guida

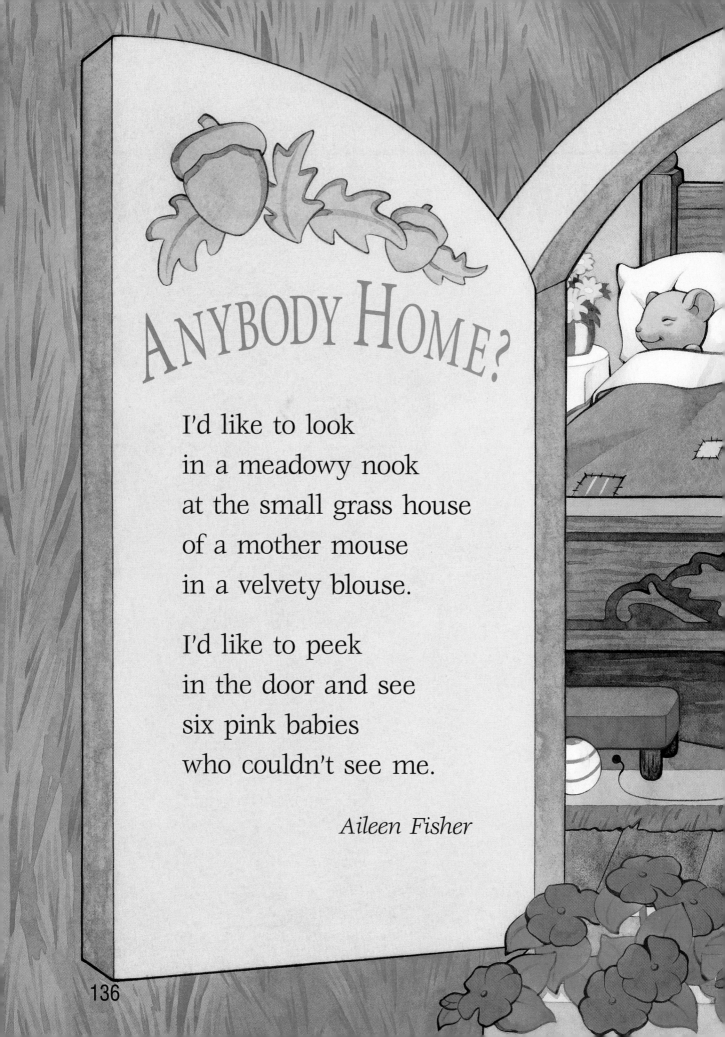

ANYBODY HOME?

I'd like to look
in a meadowy nook
at the small grass house
of a mother mouse
in a velvety blouse.

I'd like to peek
in the door and see
six pink babies
who couldn't see me.

Aileen Fisher

Meet the Red Fox

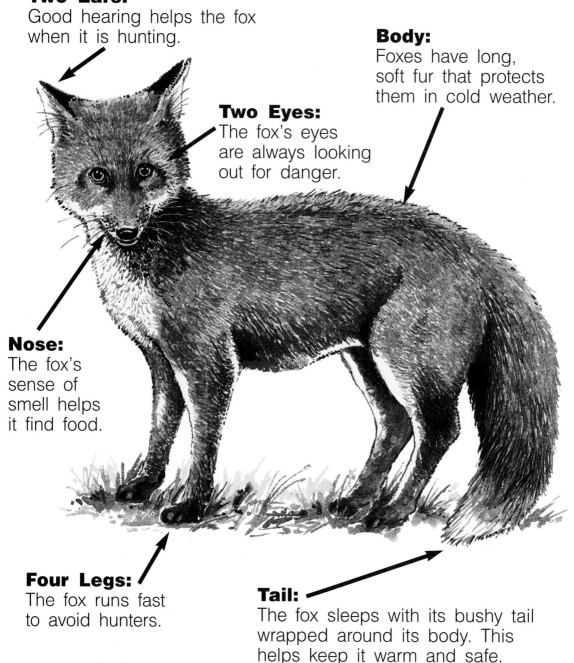

Two Ears:
Good hearing helps the fox
when it is hunting.

Two Eyes:
The fox's eyes
are always looking
out for danger.

Body:
Foxes have long,
soft fur that protects
them in cold weather.

Nose:
The fox's
sense of
smell helps
it find food.

Four Legs:
The fox runs fast
to avoid hunters.

Tail:
The fox sleeps with its bushy tail
wrapped around its body. This
helps keep it warm and safe.

DIAGRAMS

Life in a Pond

willow tree

dragonfly

heron

alder tree

squirrel

plant life

water lilies

raccoon

bullfrog

turtles

plant life

crayfish

fish

DIRECTIONS

PAPER-PLATE MASKS

Here's what you will need:

- paper plate
- scissors
- bathroom tissue roll
- tape
- paint or markers

- glue
- construction paper, feathers, pipe cleaners, and other craft materials
- yarn

Make an Animal Mask

1.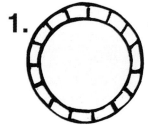
- Think of an animal mask to make.

2.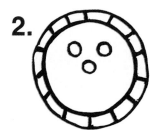
- Hold a paper plate against your face.
- Have a friend make marks for your eyes and nose.
- Then cut two eye holes and a small nose hole.

3.
- Tape the tissue roll to the plate.
- To make a beak, flatten the roll.

4.
- Trim away the bottom of the plate.

5.
- Paint or color the mask.
- Add whiskers, ears, feathers, or other items.

6.
- Poke holes at the sides of the mask.
- Pull yarn through the holes and tape down the ends.

DIRECTIONS

CHICK IN A NEST

Materials

- cardboard egg carton
- scissors
- glue
- yarn, two colors
- construction paper
- paint

Directions

1.
- Cut one cup from the egg carton.
- Spread glue around the outside.
- Wind a piece of yarn around the cup.
- Let the cup dry.

2.
- Cut the second color of yarn into short pieces.
- Glue them inside the cup.
- You now have straw or twigs in a nest.

3.
- Cut a new cup from the egg carton.
- Turn it upside down.
- Make sure it fits in the nest.
- You can cut the new cup down until it does fit.

4.
- Paint the new cup.
- Let it dry.
- You now have the chick's body.

5.
- Cut the eyes and a beak from construction paper.
- Glue them to the painted cup.
- Then, glue the chick inside the nest.

MAPS

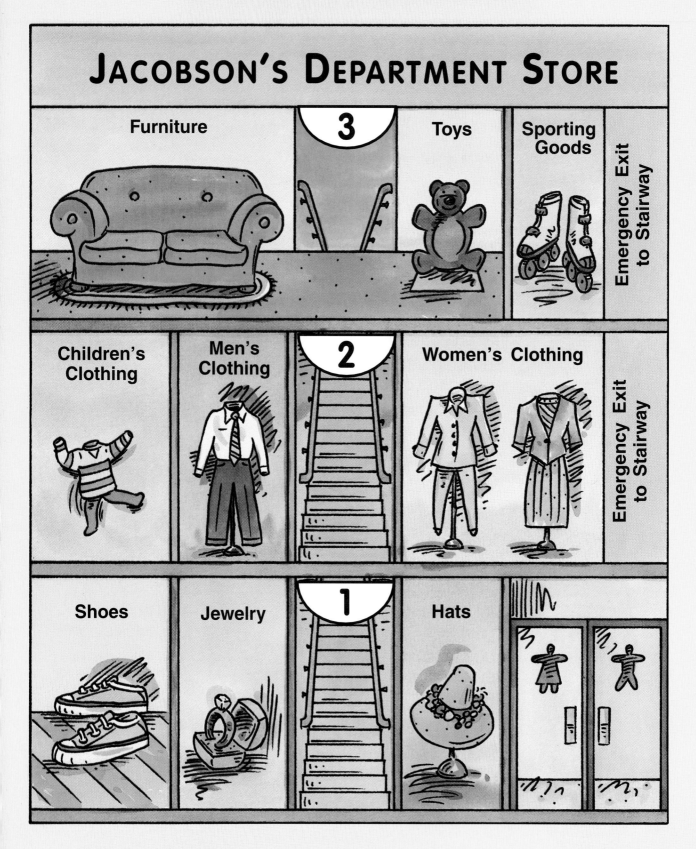

JACOBSON'S DEPARTMENT STORE

Furniture

3

Toys

Sporting Goods

Emergency Exit to Stairway

Children's Clothing

Men's Clothing

2

Women's Clothing

Emergency Exit to Stairway

Shoes

Jewelry

1

Hats

FREE PUPPIES

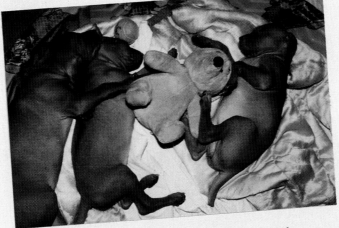

Need to find good home for 3 puppies!

OPEN HOUSE

This Saturday afternoon
3:00 - 6:00 P.M.

3 Greenwood Lane
(corner of Main Street)

For more information call:
555-8099 after 3:00 P.M.

GLOS

his glossary can help you to find out the meanings of words in this book that you may not know.

SARY

The words are listed in alphabetical order. Guide words at the top of each page tell you the first and last words on the page.

Aa

across

Across means from one side to the other. Everyone ice-skated **across** the pond and then back again.

across

afternoon

Afternoon is the part of the day between noon and evening. Our school day ends at 3 o'clock in the **afternoon**. ▲ **afternoons.**

agree

When you **agree** with someone, you think or feel the same way that person does. We will **agree** to name our new cat Tabby. ▲ **agreed, agreeing.**

alligator

An **alligator** is an animal with a long body, a long tail, and short legs. It has a large mouth with many sharp teeth. **Alligators** live in rivers and swamps. ▲ **alligators.**

alligator

along

Along means together with someone or something. Do you want to come **along** with me to the park?

animal

An **animal** is anything that is alive that is not a plant and can move around by itself. A boy, a girl, a cow, a bird, a fish, and a snake are all **animals.** ▲ **animals.**

any

Any means one or some of something. You may use **any** crayon in this box.

Bb

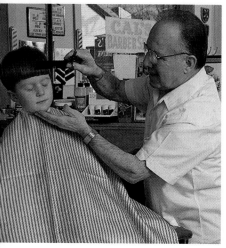

barber

barber

A **barber** is a person who cuts hair. Mom took me to the **barber** because my hair was too long. ▲ **barbers.**

beautiful

When something is **beautiful,** it is very pretty to look at or listen to. The sunset last night was **beautiful.**

body

A **body** is all of a person or an animal. An elephant has a huge, heavy **body.** ▲ **bodies.**

brother

Your **brother** is a boy who has the same mother and father as you do. My **brother** feeds the dog when he gets home from school. ▲ **brothers.**

bush

A **bush** is a plant that is smaller than a tree. A **bush** has many branches. Roses and some kinds of berries grow on **bushes.** ▲ **bushes.**

butterfly

A **butterfly** is an insect that has four large wings with bright colors. A **butterfly** landed on the flower. ▲ **butterflies.**

butterfly

Cc

call

Call means to say something in a loud voice. Dad will **call** us when dinner is ready. ▲ **called, calling.**

caterpillar

A **caterpillar** is a baby butterfly that has a soft, long, round body, no wings, many legs, and is often furry. The **caterpillar** crawled onto her finger. ▲ **caterpillars.**

caterpillar

clothes

People wear **clothes** to cover their bodies. Coats, dresses, pants, and jackets are kinds of **clothes.**

cook

A **cook** is a person who makes food ready to eat. My mom is a good **cook.** ▲ **cooked, cooking.**

count

Count means to find out how many of something there are. Let's **count** how many apples we picked. ▲ **counted, counting.**

count

Dd

danger

Danger means that something could happen to hurt you. The bird escaped **danger** by flying away from the cat. ▲ **dangers.**

drink

A **drink** is a liquid you put in your mouth and swallow. Tim's favorite **drink** is milk. ▲ **drinks.**

ear

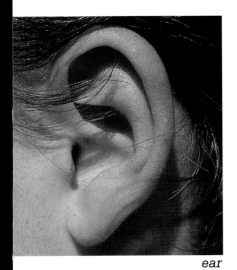

ear

An **ear** is the part of the body that you hear with. There is one **ear** on each side of your head. ▲ **ears.**

elephant

An **elephant** is the biggest and strongest animal that lives on land. It has thick gray skin and a long nose called a trunk. We saw an **elephant** at the zoo. ▲ **elephants.**

everywhere

Everywhere means in all places. Betty looked **everywhere** in the house for her shoes.

G7

eye

An **eye** is the part of the body that you see with. The baby closed his **eyes** and went to sleep. ▲ **eyes.**

fall

Fall means to come down from a place. I like to watch the rain **fall** from the sky. ▲ **fell, fallen, falling.**

fall

farther

When something is **farther** away it means that it is a greater distance away. Rae's paper plane flew **farther** than Tommy's did.

food

Food is what we eat. Everything that lives needs **food** to grow. ▲ **foods.**

give

Give means to let someone have something to keep. Suzy **gives** toys to her little sister. ▲ **gave, given, giving.**

great

Great means large or a lot. A **great** number of people voted in the election. ▲ **greater, greatest.**

head

head

The **head** is the part of the body above the neck. Eyes, ears, nose, and mouth are all parts of the **head.** ▲ **heads.**

G9

Jj

jester

A **jester** was a person long ago who played jokes and made people laugh. The king and queen laughed at the silly **jester.** ▲ **jesters.**

Kk

king

kind

Kind means a group of things that are alike in some way. Apples are a **kind** of fruit. ▲ **kinds.**

king

A **king** is a man who rules a country. I like the story about a **king** and a queen who live in a castle. ▲ **kings.**

G10

knight

Long ago, a **knight** was a soldier for a king or queen. **Knights** wore armor and rode horses. ▲ **knights.**

knight

Ll

leg

A **leg** is a part of the body that you stand or walk on. People and animals stand and walk on their **legs.** ▲ **legs.**

Mm

morning

Morning is the part of the day before noon. I like to wake up early in the **morning** when the sun shines through my window. ▲ **mornings.**

G11

N n

nest

A **nest** is a bird's house. Birds build their **nests** with leaves, sticks, and mud. ▲ **nests.**

nest

nice

When something is **nice,** it makes you feel good. The sun was shining, and it was a **nice** day. ▲ **nicer, nicest.**

nose

Your **nose** is in the center of your face. You breathe and smell things through your **nose.** ▲ **noses.**

Pp

pair

A **pair** means two things that go together or something that has two legs or two parts. I need a new **pair** of socks. ▲ **pairs.**

pants

Pants are clothes that you wear on the bottom half of your body. Pants cover each leg separately. Jamie wore new **pants** to the party.

pond

A **pond** is a small lake with land all around it. The **pond** in back of my house has fish and frogs in it. ▲ **ponds.**

pond

prince

A **prince** is the son of a king or queen. Someday the **prince** will become a king. ▲ **princes.**

Qq

queen

queen

A **queen** is a woman who rules a country. The **queen** waved to the people as she rode in the carriage. ▲ **queens.**

Rr

return

Return means to come back or to go back. My cousin will **return** to France after visiting us. ▲ **returned, returning.**

S s

silly

When someone or something is **silly,** it makes us laugh. That **silly** clown did such funny things. ▲ **sillier, silliest.**

silly

sister

Your **sister** is a girl who has the same mother and father as you do. My **sister** and I both have blue eyes. ▲ **sisters.**

sock

A **sock** is a soft cover for your foot. **Socks** are worn inside shoes. ▲ **socks.**

strange

Strange means very different from what you expect. Joseph drew a picture of a **strange** animal with red ears.

▲ **stranger, strangest.**

swim

Swim means to move in the water by using arms, legs, fins, or a tail. People **swim** using their arms and legs. ▲ **swam, swum, swimming.**

swim

Tt

tail

A **tail** is the part of an animal's body at the end of the back. Cats, dogs, and fish have **tails.** ▲ **tails.**

trouble

Trouble means that something is hard to do or might even be dangerous. Pat had **trouble** putting on his boots. ▲ **troubles.**

trunk

A **trunk** is the long nose of an elephant. Elephants use their **trunks** to pick things up. ▲ **trunks.**

trunk

turn

A **turn** is a person's time to do something. It is Dan's **turn** to hit the ball. ▲ **turns.**

V v

visit

Visit means to go to see someone.
Uncle Paul came to **visit** us. ▲ **visited,
visiting.**

W w

water

water

Water is the liquid that falls to the
ground as rain. It is in oceans, lakes,
rivers, and ponds. We all need **water**
to live.

waterproof

When something is **waterproof,** it will
not let water go through it. Billy's
raincoat was **waterproof.**

whole

When something is **whole,** it has no parts missing from it. Myra read the **whole** book in just two days.

wing

A **wing** is the part of a butterfly or insect that helps it to fly. The **wings** of the butterfly are very beautiful.

▲ **wings.**

woods

An area with a lot of trees and other plants is called a **woods.** We walked through the **woods.**

woods

ACKNOWLEDGMENTS

The publisher gratefully acknowledges permission to reprint the following copyrighted material:

Entire text, art, and cover of ANY KIND OF DOG by Lynn Reiser. Copyright (c) 1992 by Lynn Whisnant Reisner. By permission of Greenwillow Books, a division of William Morrow and Company.

"Anybody Home?" by Aileen Fisher. By permission of the author, who controls the rights..

"The Cloud" by Emma Pérez. Reprinted by permission.

"The Elephant's Trunk" reprinted from the September, Series II issue of *YOUR BIG BACKYARD,* with the permission of the publisher, the National Wildlife Federation. Copyright 1981 by the National Wildlife Federation.

"The Family Circus" by Bil Keane, from THROUGH THE YEARS WITH THE FAMILY CIRCUS. Copyright © 1992 by Bil Keane Inc., published by Ballantine Books, a division of Random House, Inc. Reprinted by permission.

"First Snow" by Marie Louise Allen. Reprinted by permission.

"The Folk Who Live in Backward Town" reprinted by permission of Gina Maccoby Literary Agency. Copyright © 1959 by Mary Ann Hoberman, renewed 1987.

"Hattie and the Fox" is the entire text and all artwork from HATTIE AND THE FOX by Mem Fox. Text copyright (c) 1986 by Mem Fox. Illustrations copyright (c) 1986 by Patricia Mullins. Reprinted with permission of Simon & Schuster Books For Young Children, Simon & Schuster Children's Publishing Division.

The book cover of LON PO PO: A RED RIDING HOOD STORY FROM CHINA by Ed Young. Copyright © 1989 by Ed Young. Published by the Putnam Publishing Group. Reprinted by permission.

"Magic in Mother Gooseland" by Sally Lucas, is from HIGHLIGHTS FOR CHILDREN July/August 1993 issue. Copyright © 1993 by Highlights for Children, Inc., Columbus, Ohio.

"One Monday Morning" by Uri Shulevitz. Copyright (c) 1974 by Uri Shulevitz. Reprinted with permission of Atheneum Books for Young Readers, Simon & Schuster Children's Publishing Division.

"Open" by Chikaoka Saori. Reprinted by permission.

"Seven Blind Mice" by Ed Young. Copyright © 1992, by Ed Young, published by Philomel Books. Reprinted by permission of the publisher.

"Seven Sillies" by Joyce Dunbar, illustrated by Chris Downing, Copyright © 1993, by Joyce Dunbar and Chris Downing. Reprinted by permission of Andersen Press, Ltd.

Text of "Something Big Has Been Here" from SOMETHING BIG HAS BEEN HERE by Jack Prelutsky. Text copyright © 1990 by Jack Prelutsky. By permission of Greenwillow Books, a division of William Morrow and Company, Inc.

Entire text, art, and cover of THE STORY OF CHICKEN LICKEN by Jan Ormerod. Copyright (c) 1985 by Jan Ormerod. By permission of Lothrop, Lee & Shepard Books, a division of William Morrow and Company, Inc.

"Surprises" by Jean Conder Soule. Reprinted by permission.

Entire text, art, and cover of THE SURPRISE FAMILY by Lynn Reiser. Copyright (c) 1994 by Lynn Whisnant Reiser. By permission of Greenwillow Books, a division of William Morrow and Company.

"Things That Happen" by Felice Holman, reprinted by permission of the author from AT THE TOP OF MY VOICE AND OTHER POEMS, Charles Scribner's Sons. Copyright © 1970 Felice Holman.

"A Wild Alphabet" reprinted from the June, Series I issue of Your Big Backyard, with the permission of the publisher, the National Wildlife Federation. Copyright (c) 1980 by the National Wildlife Federation.

"You'll Soon Grow into Them, Titch" Text & Art from YOU'LL SOON GROW INTO THEM TITCH by Pat Hutchins. Copyright © 1983 by Pat Hutchins. By permission of Greenwillow Books, a division of William Morrow & Company, Inc.

COVER DESIGN: Carbone Smolan Associates
COVER ILLUSTRATION: Kathleen O'Malley

DESIGN CREDITS
Carbone Smolan Associates, front matter 8-9
Bill Smith Studio, 70-71, 134-135
Function Thru Form, Inc., 138-143

ILLUSTRATION CREDITS
Unit 1: Kathleen O'Malley, 8-9; Meryl Henderson, 44-45; Gary Krejca, 70 (title); Lisa Berrett, 136-137. **Reading Resources:** Denny Bond, 138-139 Nell Davis, 140-141; Randy Chewning, 142; Felicia Telsey, 143. **Glossary:** Bob Pepper, G2, G6, G9, G10, G14, G16; Will and Cory Nelson, G3, G4-G5, G12.

PHOTOGRAPHY CREDITS

All photographs are by the Macmillan/McGraw-Hill School Division (MMSD) except as noted below.

42: Courtesy of Bradbury Press. 43: Courtesy of Ashton Scholastic. 69: J. Dury. 70-71: Kjell B. Sandved. 72-73 Darryl Torchler/Tony Stone Images. 106-107: Barbara Conn/F-Stop Pictures. 108: Courtesy of Jan Ormerod: 143: t.l. Monica Stevenson for MMSD. **Glossary:** GO: Inga Spence/Tom Stack & Associates; Superstock; Comstock. G1: Jack Van Antwerp/The Stock Market; Craig Tuttle/The Stock Market; Richard Gross/The Stock Market. G4: t.l. Kim Robbie/The Stock Market. G7: t.l. Bob Daemmrich/Stock Boston. G8: m. Roy Morsch/The Stock Market. G11: t.l. Charles Mahaux/The Image Bank. G15: t. Ted Horowitz/The Stock Market. G17: Tim Davis/Tony Stone Images. G18: m. Uniphoto, Inc. G19: b. Eastcott/Tthe Image Works.